LISA HOUCK
BRIGHT WORLD

COLORING BOOK

American artist Lisa Houck (b. 1953) expresses her view of nature through wild and vibrant paintings, ceramics, prints, and mosaics. The creatures and plants that appear in her watercolors and oil paintings seem to be curling, swirling, twirling, and unfurling. She uses bright colors for her birds, butterflies, trees, lizards, monkeys, and fish as they live amidst the hills, buildings, or waves. Houck uses a combination of bold textures and soft washes of watercolor to make some parts stand out and other parts fade into the background. Big things seem small and small things seem big in Houck's paintings, where a tulip or a flower pot might easily dwarf a tiny house. In Houck's magical worlds, textures, shapes, and colors make quilt-like scenes of lush gardens and cozy towns, arid deserts and busy seascapes.

When you color in the line drawings, you can copy the colors of the original artwork shown on the inside covers, or you can come up with your own combinations. We've also left a blank page in the back of the book where you can create your very own bright world. What do you notice most in nature? Remember to include some dots or swirls, plants or animals, houses or hills.

Pomegranate

The drawings in this coloring book are based on the following artwork by Lisa Houck (American, b. 1953):

1. *A Bug's Life*, watercolor, 14 x 20 in.

2. *Above It All*, oil on wood, 24 x 24 in.

3. *The Garden Is Taking Over*, watercolor, 9 x 12 in.

4. *Life in the Garden*, watercolor, 9 x 6 in.

5. *Landscape with Lizard*, oil on wood, 24 x 36 in.

6. *Being Blue*, oil on wood, 10 x 10 in.

7. *My Yellow Friend*, watercolor, 9 x 6 in.

8. *Landscape with Red Bug*, oil on wood, 20 x 30 in.

9. *Beside the Point*, oil on wood, 24 x 24 in.

10. *On the Lookout*, watercolor, 9 x 6 in.

11. *Container Garden*, oil on wood, 18 x 24 in.

12. *Fiddleheads Unfurling*, watercolor, 9 x 6 in.

13. *Two Swallowtails*, oil on wood, 20 x 30 in.

14. *The Curious Ones*, watercolor, 22 x 30 in.

15. *Nest and Nuthatch*, oil on wood, 20 x 20 in.

16. *Landscape with Visitors*, oil on wood, 24 x 36 in.

17. *The Edge of the Woods*, watercolor, 9 x 6 in.

18. *Small Town Life*, watercolor, 6 x 9 in.

19. *Showy Species*, oil on wood, 18 x 24 in.

20. *Urban Woodpecker*, watercolor, 9 x 6 in.

21. *Short and Sweet*, oil on wood, 22 x 30 in.

22. *Welcome to My House*, watercolor, 22 x 30 in.

Pomegranate Communications, Inc.
19018 NE Portal Way, Portland OR 97230
800 227 1428   www.pomegranate.com

Artwork © 2015 Lisa Houck
www.lisahouck.com
Line drawings © Pomegranate Communications, Inc.

Item No. CB167

Designed by Tristen Jackman. Line drawings by Jennifer Messinger.

Printed in Korea

24 23 22 21 20 19 18 17 16 15   11 10 9 8 7 6 5 4 3 2

Distributed by Pomegranate Europe Ltd.
Unit 1, Heathcote Business Centre, Hurlbutt Road
Warwick, Warwickshire CV34 6TD, UK
[+44] 0 1926 430111
sales@pomeurope.co.uk

2. Above It All

3. The Garden Is Taking Over

4. *Life in the Garden*

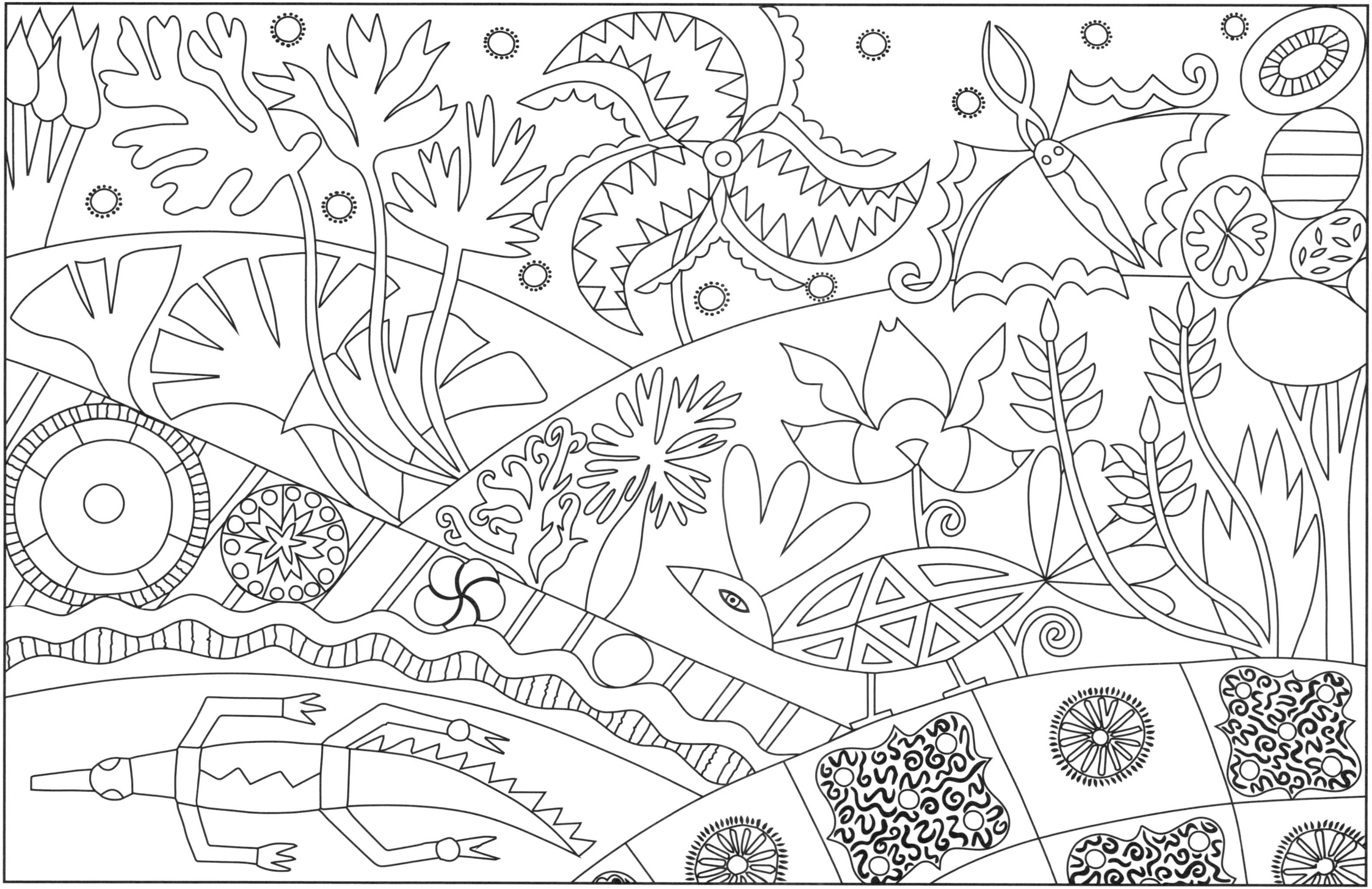

5. *Landscape with Lizard*

6. *Being Blue*

7. *My Yellow Friend*

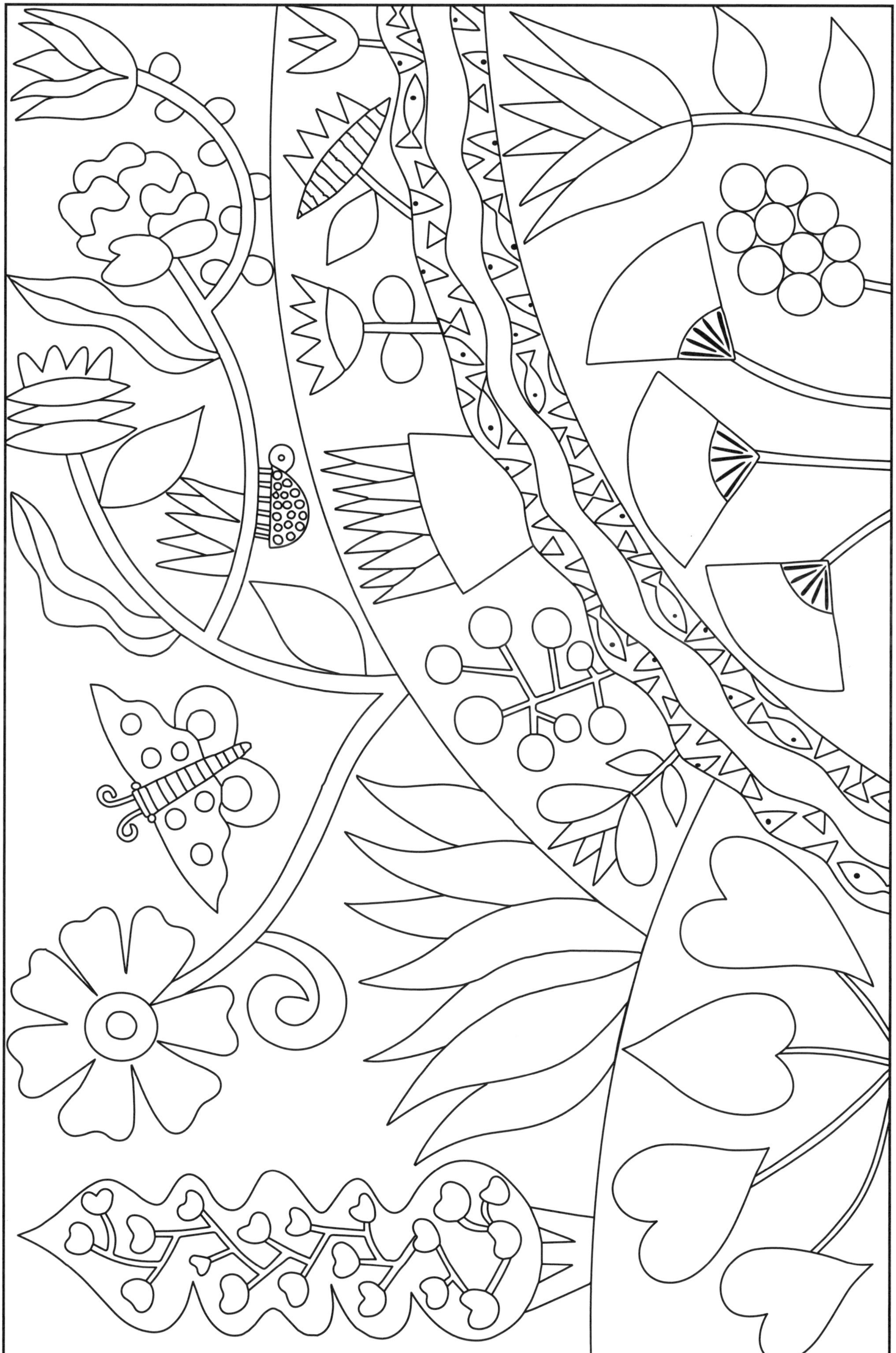

8. Landscape with Red Bug

9. Beside the Point

10. On the Lookout

11. Container Garden

12. Fiddleheads Unfurling

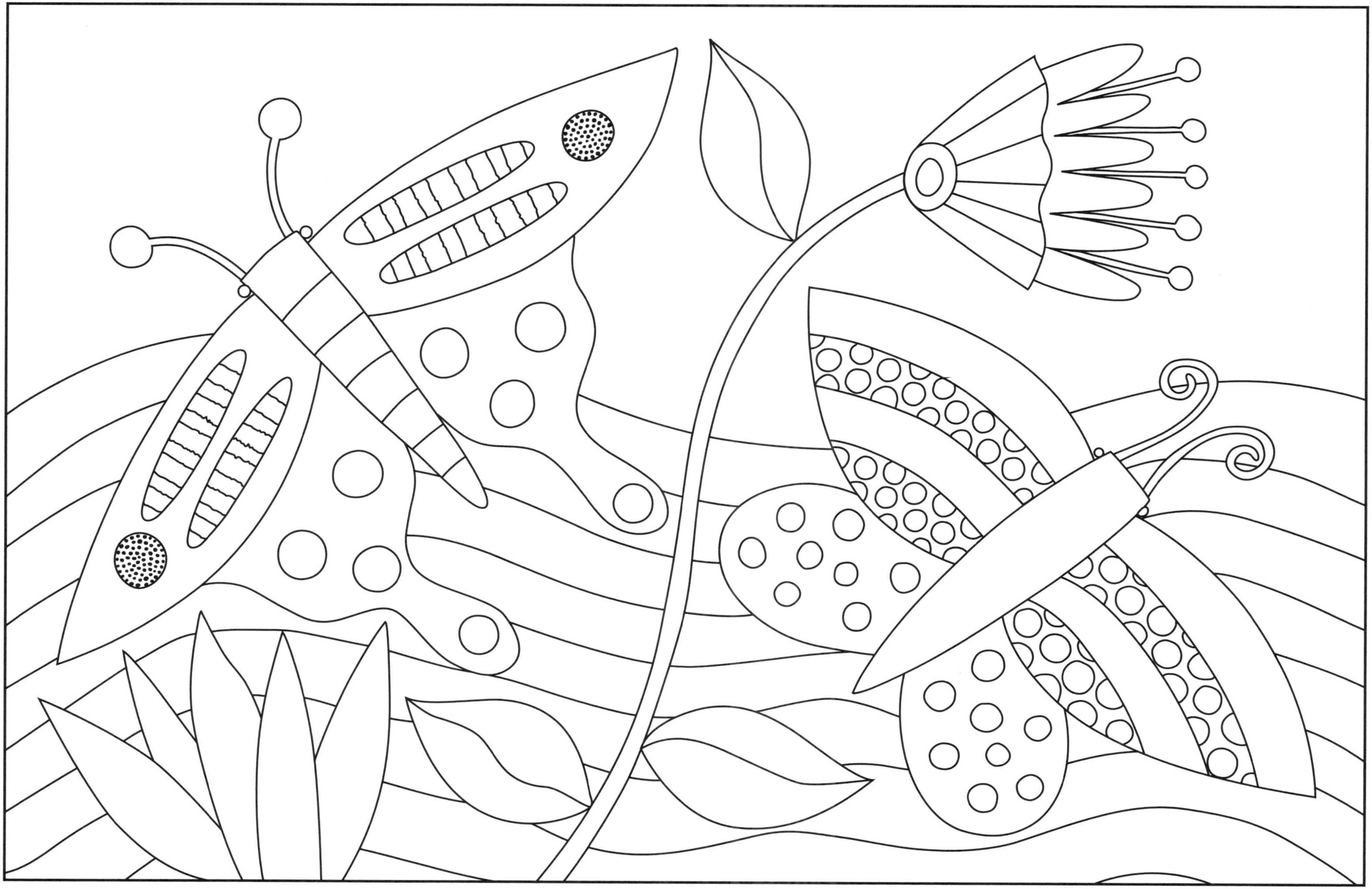

13. *Two Swallowtails*

14. The Curious Ones

15. *Nest and Nuthatch*

16. *Landscape with Visitors*

17. The Edge of the Woods

18. *Small Town Life*

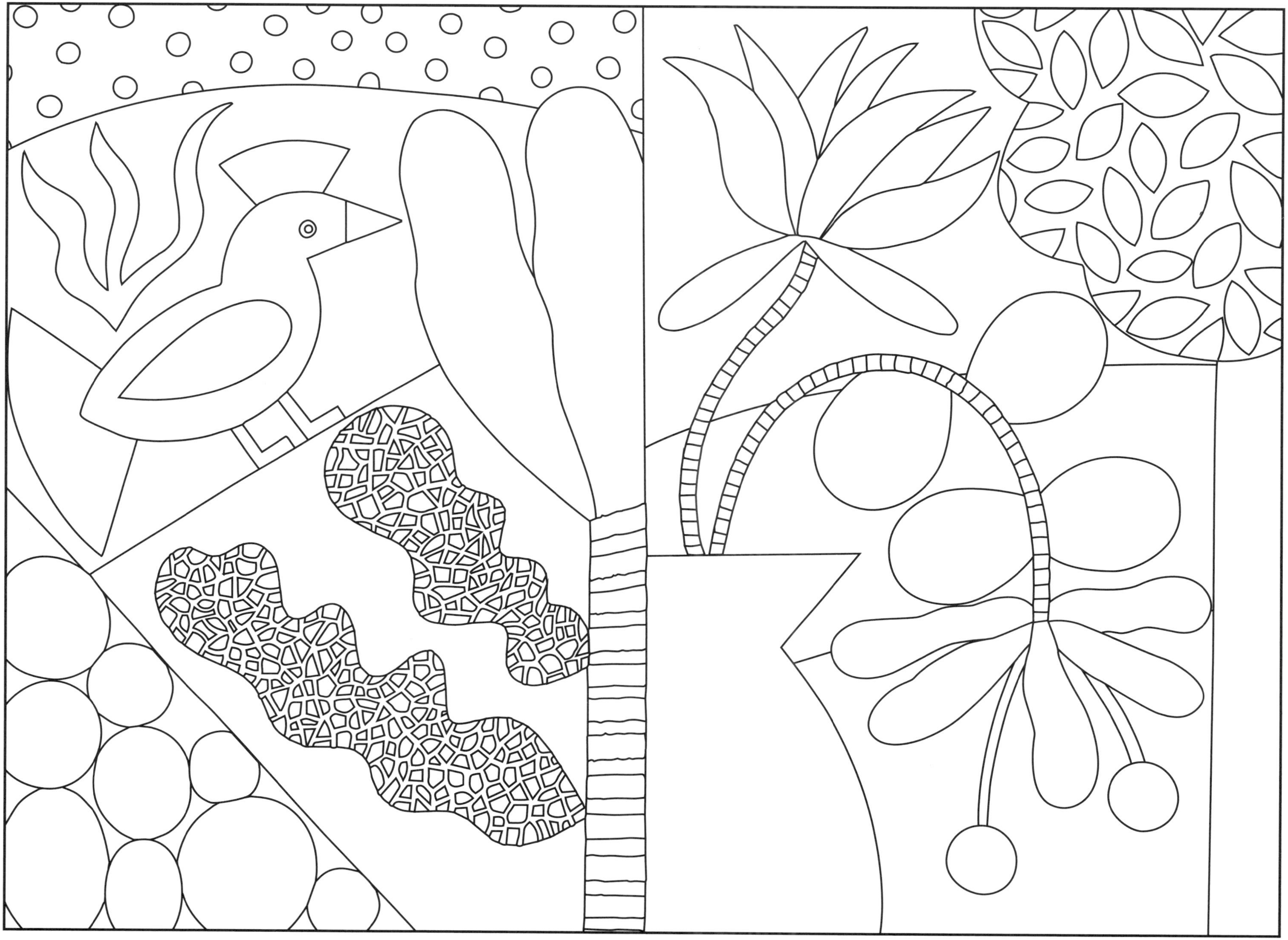

19. *Showy Species*

20. *Urban Woodpecker*

21. *Short and Sweet*

Draw and color your own picture here!